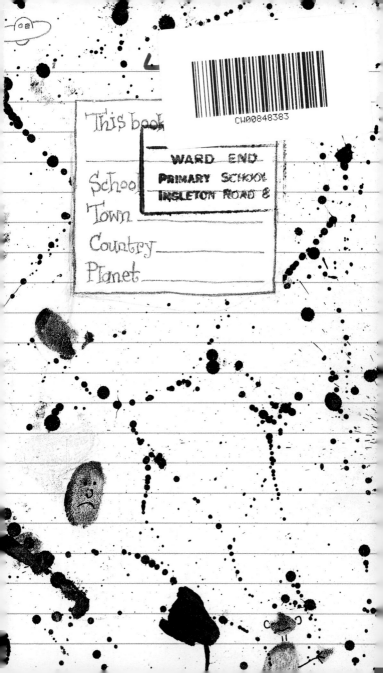

This book

School

Town

Country

Planet

CW00848383

If you enjoy SCHOOL, you'll love...
SPOOKS
MONSTERS
VAMPIRES
WITCHES
PIRATES
All published in this series by
Collins Children's Books.

SCHOOL was first published in Great Britain
in 1994 by HarperCollins Publishers Ltd
First published in this format in 1996
by HarperCollins Publishers Ltd,
77-85 Fulham Palace Road, Hammersmith,
London, W6 8JB
1 3 5 7 9 10 8 6 4 2
Copyright © Colin and Jacqui Hawkins 1994
The authors assert the moral right to be
identified as the authors of the work.
ISBN: 0 00 198170-6
This book is set in Galliard 12/16
Printed in Hong Kong

School

Colin and Jacqui Hawkins.

Collins

An Imprint of HarperCollins*Publishers*

Kids (Types).

Bully

Thick stupid kid who goes round beating up little or soft kids. Has no real friends, only toadies (see Toadies). Bullies do not like being stared at so try not to look at them. Bullies usually have Whopper or Stinker put before their name, like Stinker Smith or Whopper Wilson. To get even with a bully, put 'Kick Me Hard' on paper on his/her back.

Bully Joke:
How do bullies learn to get what they want?
By trial and terror.

Typical bully greeting →

Gimme those sweets or I'll bash you.

<u>Note</u> this is a girl bully, boy bullies are just as ugly

School Proverb
Laugh and the school
laughs with you.
Laugh at the school bully
and you laugh alone.

A friend in need
...is a pest.

...I won't
tell.

Sneak, baby, sneak
Your pants do leak!

Toadie

A toadie is someone who sneaks or blabs to
teacher. Also called a spoilsport, slimy snake,
rat or telltale. Never, never trust a toadie.

Tell tale tit
Your tongue will be split
And all the dogs in town
Shall have a little bit.

Blabbermouth

Someone who can't keep their gob
(mouth) shut. Teller of secrets.
(see Toadie, see Creep, see Sneak)

Are You a Teacher's Pet?

Check out the following:
Five points for every **YES** answered.

Do You have..?

Brain that likes Latin, Alge
Trigonometry, Geometry

Alert clear eyes

Clean behind ears

Face clean and shiny (no zits or snot)

Clean cuffs

Bag full of finished homework (All neat and tidy. <u>No</u> blots)

Clea
nec

Clean knees with no bump or bruises

Socks pulled up

No mud on shoes. Sensible type. (No trainers)

Clean, shiny shoes

Shoelaces done up

Teacher's Titter

What is the most popular answer to Teacher's questions?

I don't know.

Correct.

Joke to Teacher's — Pet —

Are you a P.L.P.?
No!
You're quite right.
You're not a proper looking person.

- Hair neatly combed and brushed. (No nits)

— Clean inside ears (no potatoes)

I'm a teacher's Pet

- Tie always neatly knotted

— Clean shirt (ironed)

— No ink on fingers

— Clean fingernails

—Apple for teacher

How do you score?

SCORE:

80-100   Super Teacher's Pet
60-80   Teacher's Pet
40-60   Form Prefect Type
20-40   Nearly a Goodie
5-20   Toadie Type
Zero and below   Average Kid

Why is that boy in a cage?

Because he's a Teacher's pet.

Creep

Kid who says really crawly, cringy, squirmy, wormy things to teachers. (Yuk!)

Crybaby

Kids who weep are called crybabies, diddums, snivellers, blubber-mouths or sissies.

Hay is for horses
Straw is for cows
Milk is for babies
that cry out loud.

Jelly baby

Advice to crybabies:
Go back to your bottle.
Don't make it wet on a dry day.

Baby Bawlings
Crybaby, cry
Put your finger in your eye
Hang him on a lamppost
And leave him there
to dry.

Sir, Sir, I just... wanted to say what a really excellent Maths lesson that was, Sir.

Is your hair wet? There's a big drip under it.

Twit Quips
You're daft and dithering,
Wipe your chin and stop dribbling.

You're daft, you're potty,
You're made of treacle toffee!

Terrible Twittish Jokes
in a shoe box?
No, but a tin can.

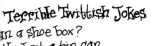

Why do twits eat biscuits?

Because they're CRACKERS!

Twit
Someone who is daft, loco, cracked, barmy, batty or dopey. Not all there.

I'm all here

Goody-Goody (Prefect*Perfect)

These kids are rarely seen in school. But if you spot any they will have rings of light (halos) over their heads like angels or baby Jesus.

* Perfect kids, goody-goodies and swots make perfect prefects

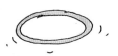

I'm as good as gold

Goody-goodies usually win lots of prizes.

Goody giggle:

What did the cannibal say when he saw Santa Claus?

Goody, goody, Christmas dinner

Please sir, I feel a bit strange

Weird Joke:
Why did Cyclops give up teaching? Because he only had one pupil.

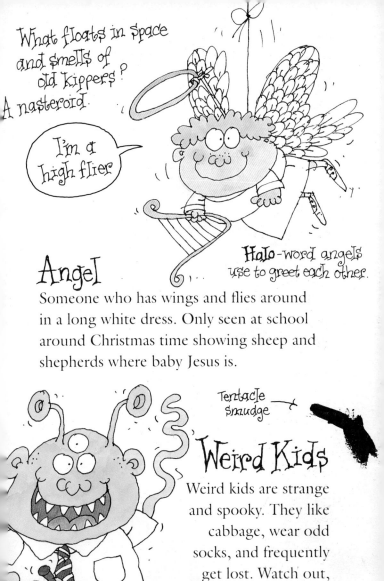

What floats in space and smells of old kippers? A nasteroid.

I'm a high flier

Halo - word angels use to greet each other.

Angel

Someone who has wings and flies around in a long white dress. Only seen at school around Christmas time showing sheep and shepherds where baby Jesus is.

Tentacle smudge

Weird Kids

Weird kids are strange and spooky. They like cabbage, wear odd socks, and frequently get lost. Watch out, some teachers are also weird. (Check socks)

11

Weird Kids can read upside down.

Evil Kids

Evil kids have power to make you do things that you don't want to do. These are the troublemakers who never get blamed. Look for a 666 on the back of the head, especially if they are called Damien.

Dunce Ditty

Dunce Dunce double D
Cannot learn his ABC
Put a cap on, then you'll see
What a silly boy is he.

Dunce

Foolscap:
a hat with a large D on it.

In the olden days (when teacher was young) any kid that didn't know his lessons was called a dunce. He was made to wear a dunce's hat and stand in a corner until he knew the answers. (This could take a long time.)

12

Zombies

These are the kids who stay up all night watching TV. They have a deadpan expression and move very slowly.

Smokers

Stupid kids think smoking is cool but spend a lot of time going green and feeling sick. They also get brown teeth, brown fingers and they never grow and they die. Smoking is usually done in the bogs or behind the bike-sheds.

Gasper's Gags:
It's not the cough that carries you off.
It's the coffin they carry you off in.

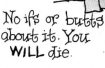

No ifs or butts about it. You **WILL** die.

Vulcan

Big-eared character from Star Trek. Rarely seen at school. Also a know-all.

I know it all

What illness did everyone on the Enterprise catch Chicken spocks.

It isn't a joke. Kids that smoke CROAK!

What did the school sing when the headmaster stopped smoking?
Wheeze a jolly good fellow.

OTHER TYPES

SNEAK Kid who blabs to teacher (see Toadie).

WHIZZ KID Someone who is top of the class. (Usually teacher's pet).

CLEVER DICK Smart, brainy kid.

COPY-CAT A kid who imitates.
Copy-cat, stole a rat.
Put it in his Sunday hat.

CRIBBER Someone who copies someone else's work.

NOSY PARKER Also known as flap-ears, Keyhole Kate.
ANSWER THEIR QUESTIONS WITH:
i) Nosy parker, squashed tomato.
ii) Quizzy flies never grow wise.
iii) Ask no questions and you'll be told no lies.

SWOT A kid who works very hard.

COWARDY-CUSTARD
Any kid who will not take part in a dare. Also called a Yellow Belly or Scaredy-Cat.
Cowardy-cowardy custard
Yellow as mustard.

Lessons and Learning

Lessons are a cruel rotten way to spend the best days of your life.

Please God don't let he ask me...

Hands Up

This is what happens when teacher asks a question in class like, "What's the square root of 14 trillion and thirty one?". The kids that know the answer go "Sir! Sir! I know Sir!" and put their hands up. The kids that don't know look stupid and worried, so cruel teachers always ask them. Remember, even if you don't know the answer, put up your hand and go "Sir! Sir! I know Sir!" and wave it about a lot. Teachers never ask kids who know the answer, or appear to know.

Clock Watching

School clocks move extremely slowly in lesson time. Try not to watch them as this slows them down even more.

Harry left school with regret. He was sorry he ever had to go.

Recommended Reading:
LAST DAY OF SCHOOL
By Gladys Friday.

Absent

This is when someone is not here, or away, or missing from school (see Sick Note and Diseases). Some kids and some teachers are absent in the mind. If your name is Sharon and teacher calls you George, teacher's mind has gone absent.

Absence makes the heart grow fonder ♡

Brains

Brains are what you use for school work.
The bigger your brain the better you
are at knowing the answers to the things
teachers ask you.

Zero

Zilch. Nothing. No mark. Lowest score
you can get in a school test. Really wicked
(cool). But teachers, Mums and Dads
not impressed.

Swot (Mega brain)

I know, sir!

Swot's jot: You Clot!
Why Sir? What?
This blot. It's snot!

Lesson Lore

1. Always be on time for class. Teachers hate late learners.
2. Ignore stupid kids when they pull silly faces at you behind Teacher's back.
3. Teachers hate giggling, gurgling, tittering, hooting, sniggering, chortling, chuckling, and smirking.
4. <u>Never</u> forget your homework.
5. Don't (TO EVERYTHING)

X Mark

Mark that looks like a kiss. If your work comes back with lots of x's this does not mean that teacher's in love with you. This is not a kiss. This means your work is wrong.

Brill!

Teachers usually put See Me! when you get everything wrong.

Teacher's Teaser:
Spot the deliberate spelling mistake on this page.

Kid "napping" (dozing, kipping, snoozing.)

Sudden desperate need to go to sleep during lesson time – usually at around three o'clock in the afternoon. Some kids are really good at napping and can 'nap' for the whole of a lesson without ever being discovered. Teachers hate nappers and will rudely shout and wake up any kids they see peacefully asleep.

The Yawn
Eyes become very heavy.

Kipper: Someone who spends a lot of time sleeping.

What a thought! You go to school till you're sixteen. Teachers stay at school until they are SIXTY!

Aardvark: rarely seen at school and makes you very tired.

This is risky, teachers will notice.

Blatant napping
Head sinks slowly onto desk.

What tools do you need for Arithmetic? Multipliers.

Catnap is a brief sleep.

The book studying method

Book keeps out daylight

What do you call someone with a dictionary in their wellies? – Smarty boots

More subtle method

The head in desk method

♪ Napper's Rap ♫

Sleepin's a thing I like to do.
It's better than grammar,
and two plus two.
I shut my books. I close my eyes
And dream of burgers, ♫
shakes and fries.

Desk lid muffles snores.

The Rude Awakening

Rude remark →

YOU LAZY SLUG!!

EEK!

When does a teacher become
two teachers?
When he's beside himself.

Horror of Horrors ~ HOMEWORK

Arrgh! Cruel idea invented by mean teachers.
After a long hard day at school they give you **more**
work to lug home.
Gross! Mega Gross!

Homework Hints

Avoid doing written homework on the
bus. Teachers always recognise 'bus shake'.
Do not copy swot's homework exactly;
make a few creative mistakes, otherwise
teachers will 'suss'.

What did you
answer for
Latin homework,
Dimble?

...???
...HOMEWORK???
ARRRGH!!! I've not
done my homework!!

Swot's perfectly
everything right
homework.

8.45 School Bus
just arriving at
School gate.

HORROR!

This is the terrible sinking feeling you
get when you remember that you've
forgotten to do your homework.

22

Oooo!! ..gooo...!! I do feel ...ill ...Hooo...

All homework and no play can seriously affect your brain.

WARNING

Homework is seriously accident prone. Everything and anything can happen to homework. It will get lost, it will get thrown in the dustbin, it will get stolen by aliens...the dog will be sick on it...your mum will use it for cat litter...none of these true but terrible events will ever be believed by teachers.

Satchel full of hours of immaculately done homework

Hard Labour

After a long day's toil at school, poor kids struggle home with a typical night's homework:

double Maths,
double Geography,
triple Latin and
French irregular
verbs.

A school kid's work is never done, especially if you forget it!

23

Nits

Nits (head lice)

Nits are like a plague; like locusts, only smaller. Millions and millions of tiny creepy-crawlies suddenly live in your hair and crawl around on top of your head, making you really itch and scratch. If one kid in a school gets nits then all the kids get nits, because nits can jump and breed very quickly.

> Wot you lookin' at?

A close up → of a nit. (Not life size)

> Nits

> Wow!

Nurse or 'Nursey'

Nice lady who gives out medicine, tablets and pills when you are ill or when the Maths teacher has given you a headache. Puts ointment and plasters on playground bashings. But be warned – also tells porkie pies, especially about castor oil, syrup of figs and injections.

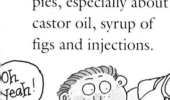

Sometimes the 'Nit Nurse' comes to school to see if any kids have nits. She uses a Nit Comb that scratches your head.

A Nit Comb or 'Bug Rake'

Nit Notes

1. Even teachers can get nits.
2. Teachers that are always finding fault with you are called nit-pickers.
3. A nit is also a dim-witted kid.

Zits

Zits are spots, boils, pimples, pustules*
or blackheads. Blackheads are horrible
blackheaded plugs of greasy gunge blocking
up pores of skin on the face or neck. Boils
are painful, pus-filled swellings. Pimples are
smaller than boils.

*pustule is an old word for pimple

Abscess
'Orrible pustulant
swelling, like a boil or
zit, but much worse.

Close up
of zit,
possibly
life size.

Teachers will avoid the
pitted and zitted as
spontaneous eruptions
can occur.

Great
zits!

Thanks
babe

Old Mr Kelly,
Had a pimple on his belly,
His wife cut it off,
And it tasted like jelly!

26

Zit Popping

1. **Finger Prod.**

2. **Finger and Thumb Method**

What do you call a teacher who has spots? Dot.

Ooze a lovely boil, then.

3. **Two Finger Press**

School Kids Proverb: A watched boil never bursts.

1. Spot on = exactly correct
2. Tight spot = difficult situation
3. High spot = best
4. In a spot = in trouble

SPOT CHECK

27

Mind Your Manners (dirty habits)

Manners

Manners are how teachers behave. At lunch time, instead of the headmaster saying to the English teacher, "Hey! Gimme the ketchup, fish-face!" he would say, "Excuse me, Miss Trout, would you be so kind as to pass me the ketchup? Thank you."

Nose-picking

Snot can be rooted out by a finger or politely blown into a tissue. Most kids pick the finger method. Kids with big nostrils can use their thumb.

**Nose Picker's
—Poem—**
Pick it.
lick it.
Roll it,
flick it.

Bogey

A piece of dried snot bunged up your nose.

Snot: also term of abuse i.e. Don't get snotty with me or You little snot!

Belching or Burping

This is the noise kids make when they drink
very quickly, open their mouths and go Burp!
Kids think this is really funny.
(WARNING: Teachers hate it.)

Gas Gag:
Did you know when
the Queen belches she
issues a royal pardon.

Recommended
Reading:
GONE WITH THE WIND
WIND IN THE WILLOWS

How do you stop
your nose from
running?
Stick out your foot
and trip it up.

Do you clean your top teeth with
a toothbrush? – Yes
What do you clean your bottom with?!

29

A Phew Nasty Niffs

Smells are common in schools. The smell and stink of cabbage, cloakrooms, armpits, B.O. (Body Odours), bad breath, bogs, cheesey feet and wind.

Why is a sausage rude?

Because it spits.

Flatulence

A gassy explosion of wind from your bum (a bottom burp). Everybody has wind, even headmasters. Some ≼3 are silent, some ≼3 are mega loud and some ≼3 are deadly poisonous. All kids are brill at ≼3 *

Bogs (Toilets)

School loos are the smelliest place in school, but the most peaceful (a good place to think). Also a hang-out for stupid kids who smoke.

green snot candles

* ≼3 - censored by Ed.

Sleeve Wipe

You can get rid of your snotty nose by using toilet paper, handkerchief, tissues, or the back of your sleeve. But it's bad manners to lick it in public.

A snotty nosed kid is either a stuck-up (posh) kid or someone with a runny nose.

NEVER
1. Spit
2. Gob
3. Drool
4. Dribble
5. Snigger
6. Sneer
7. Smirk
(at teacher)

31

Infections and Afflictions

GET AWAY FROM ME!

Infections

Lots of kids come to school with horrible
pestilent infections like measles or mumps or
bubonic plague and infect all the other kids
and the teachers. (see also Germs, Measles
and Sneezes)

Measles

Very spotty disease. Like bubonic plague
it's 'dead' infectious. (see Germs and also
Infections)

Mumps

Rotten painful disease.
Glands in neck swell
up really big. Makes
a victim look like a
hamster. (Warning:
keep well away from
anyone who looks
like a hamster.)

Vomit (school lunch re-run)

Contents of stomach ejected through mouth.
Warning signs of somebody about to vomit:*
green sweaty face, shaking shoulders and
moaning. Get out of the way quickly!
Very messy!

Faint

Woozy, dizzy feeling where you conk out in
exams when you haven't the faintest idea
what the answers are. Also a good wheeze for
getting out of lessons.

* Kids can feel sick at exam time.

33

Dangers and Diseases

SICK NOTE: Letter for teacher when you have been sick.

Sneezes

Another major irritation for teachers, especially children who sneeze germs all over them.

Teacher's Sick Joke:

Why did Smith swallow 50p, Sir?

It was his dinner money.

Here's your coffee, Sir.

SNIFF!

SNIFF!

What is a sick joke, Teacher?

Something you mustn't bring up in the conversation.

Teachers hate kids with coughs and colds especially really drippy

Germs

Tiny titchy little creatures that you can't see but they are all over school and everywhere, especially on dirty hands, dogs' breath, dogs' poo and flies' feet.

FOOT NOTE
Fungus

Some feet get fungus growing on them, especially between the toes. This is called athlete's foot (a good reason not to be an athlete). Some teachers are known as fungus face, but this is not athlete's face.

Verruca

These are painful warts on the foot or hand. Brill excuse for getting off games.

Vesuvius

MORE SICK NOTES
Warts

Lumpy growths on hands or face.

Worms

Revolting, horrible plague of little worms that live inside you. Gross! Yuk! Your dog can also get worms. Give him a worm tablet.

Teachers
Types and Traits

A teacher needs to be brainy, brawny and brave.

All-Seeing Teacher

It is well known that some teachers have eyes in the back of their heads, SO BE CAREFUL.

School Proverb

If a teacher asks you a question and you don't know the answer – mumble.

Take that gum out of your mouth, Jenkins.

"I told you to get a haircut yesterday," said the teacher.
"I did, Sir. That one!"

Pupil Power

It is also a fact that some teachers have one eye bigger than the other. This is why they are always saying, "I've got my eye on you". (Take a good look at your teacher and work out which eye is the biggest.)

I've got my eye on you.

Transfixed with terror

Pupil's Proverb

What the eye doesn't see, the teacher doesn't grieve over.

Eye Openers

I don't believe my eyes
I'm all eyes
Don't pull the wool over my eyes.
I'm up to my eyes.
This is eyewash.

Why did the teacher have to wear sunglasses?
Because her pupils were so bright.

Highly-strung Teacher (often Music Teacher)

These teachers need peace and quiet, so they will shout QUIET! a million times a day. Weird!

Teacher's Tickler
Stop scratching your head, aren't you afraid of splinters?

Overheard: QUIET, I said QUIET. Can you hear me, QUIET? Stop this riot, QUIET. QUIET, I WANT QUIET!

Pounds, shillings, pence.
Teacher has no sense
She came to school to
act the fool.
Pounds, Shillings,
pence.

GASP!

Funny Teacher

Some teachers like telling
jokes, really unfunny, really
pathetic jokes. Try to laugh.
If you can go hee! hee!
when all the other kids go,
what?? huh?? you will
become teacher's pet.
(See Teacher's Pet)
NB: Encourage your
teacher to tell more jokes.
Remember, more laughs,
less lesson.

...and to get
to the other
side. Ha! Ha!

Hee! Hee!

"Sir, my pen scratches"
"Perhaps it's got an itch."

Chalk and Talk

Has anyone seen 2B or not 2B?

Why did the school kid take her bike to school? She wanted to drive her teacher up the wall.

TWITCH

TWITCH

SNAP!

I'm off!

Tense Teacher

By the end of term many teachers have reached the end of their tether and are ready to blow their top. Beware! The danger signs to watch out for are pencil snapping, throwing chalk, twitching violently and foaming at the mouth.

Mad Teacher (The Ranter)

These teachers are classic. They generally teach Latin and Greek. These are dead languages and Latin teachers can be old and fossilized with age. Your feeble efforts at Latin verbs are enough to set them ranting and raving. Latin is mostly about Caesar and his long wars. Most kids do not understand Greek. That's why they often say, 'it's all Greek to me.'

Dictator

These teachers are very bossy, tyrannical and despotic. They want their own way all the time. Avoid these teachers as they are mega-dangerous. Danger signs to watch for: bulging eyes, red cheeks, dribbling lips and quivering jowls, and speaking very slowly in CAPITAL LETTERS (SLOWSPEAK).

NATTER NOTES
- Idle talk.
- Talk through the back of your head.
- Speak when you're spoken to.
- That will teach you a lesson.

I...HAVE...TOLD...YOU...AND...TOLD...YOU...UNTIL...I...AM...BLUE...IN...THE...FACE!

EEK!

Jabbing, pointy finger

Teacher Trivia

When lady teachers went to school, they wore big knickers so they could tuck their skirts in them for games!

Teacher Talk

Teachers must have good communication skills to get through to the thick-headed, halfwitted and gormless. Here are some typical teacher sayings. Can you think of any more?

Mad Maxims

Every time I open my mouth, some idiot starts talking.

If you shout, I cannot hear you.

* This will hurt me more than it will hurt you. (See Cane).

You will not find the answer on the ceiling

If you run, you will not get there any faster.

If you wish to talk, you must ask me first.

If you do not come back, I will not let you go again.

Let me give you a piece of my mind.

There are no dull lessons, only dull pupils.

* Said to author during painstaking research while still at school.

Touchy Teacher

Some teachers can become irritable and bad tempered, especially when marking exercise books and writing reports. Do not disturb. When they say YESSS? they mean, what do you want and why are you bothering me, you little pest.

Quick Quip
Please Sir, may I leave the room? Well, you can't take it with you.

YESSSSSSSS?!

Supply Teacher

These teachers are always coming and going. They never stay long enough to know your name, if you have homework to do, or what time of the day it is.

Where am I? Where should I be?!!

44

C.D.T. Teacher (Completely Daft Technology)

These teachers can help you to design and
make things. They usually have a tool in
hand and are known by the nickname
'Chips'. They like making stools.

Physics Teacher

These teachers often blow up when they
least expect it. They can be nervous.

Biology Teacher

These teachers are
agile and nimble.
They flit around the
classroom teaching
about birds, bees,
things that swim,
and rabbits. They
love nature and
all living creatures,
especially small furry
things and worms.

It likes you, Miss!

How many times, Jeckyll, have I told you **not** to drink that stuff?

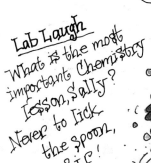

Lab Laugh
What is the most important Chemistry lesson, Sally?
Never to lick the spoon, Sir!

46

GET OFF! YOU LITTLE **!?

**!? censored by Ed.

What kind of food do pelicans eat?

Anything that fits the bill.

Oh! dear, what can the matter be? Old Miss Bilge is locked in the laboratory. She'll be there from Monday to Saturday. Nobody cares that she's there.

Chemistry Teacher

These teachers love to experiment. They are practical and good with their hands. But they will insist on telling kids the same thing over and over and over again.

Which King of England invented the fireplace? Alfred the Grate.

I heard that, Jones.

Silly old fool

History is a mystery

History Teacher

Some History teachers have very big ears. This means they have incredibly good hearing. Always whisper within 50 metres of any History teachers.

History Howler:

Can anyone tell me Gandhi's first name? Goosie, Goosie.

More History Hoots

Please Sir, I wish we lived in the olden days.
Why?
Then there wouldn't be much history to learn.

Games Teacher

Games teachers hate kids who forget their games kit. They will also seethe with rage at the sight of a sick note. They are very fit, healthy teachers who do not understand the sickly, weedy and wimpy. They rarely, if ever, take off their old track suits and smelly trainers. (Can suffer from athlete's foot.) Games lessons are also known as P.T. (Physical Torture), or P.E. (Physical Extermination).

"Sacre bleu!"

French Teacher

French teachers always speak French. This can be irritating. They do not listen unless you also speak French in class. Do not worry, add an occasional le, la or vous and you will get by.

"Miss! Miss!"

Franglais
le week-end
le T.V.
le téléphon
le hamburg

Tip: Do not mention frogs or French tarts. They do not like it

"Huh!"

What do French school kids say at the end of their school dinner?
Merci!

Silly Sonnet
I haven't a clue.
I wish I knew.
My brain is aching
My eyes are sore
Oh what is all
this learning for?

Did you hear about the teacher who kept his wife under his bed? He thinks she's a little potty.

Understanding Teachers

This is difficult. Only swots, cleverdicks and brainy kids understand what teachers are saying.

Top Tip: Always put your hand up, even if you don't know the answer. Teachers will always ask kids who don't put up their hands. (See Hands Up.)

Well...
What is it **this** time, Craig?

Maths Mirth
What is a polygon?
A dead parrot.

Why are some fractions rude?
Because they're vulgar.

Maths Teacher

Maths teachers can be mean and moody.
This is because Maths can give you a
headache. To keep a Maths teacher happy,
look keen and interested in class, even if
you are clueless. Maths teachers are good
at Mental Arithmetic. They say things like,
"Is that the sum total of your homework?"
NB: Buy a calculator. Know your Tables.

"...I was attacked by a wild bear on the bus, Sir. And it ate all my homework."

N.B. Teachers rarely-if ever-believe excuses about late or lost homework

Ghastly Giggle:
What do you call a teacher with a bus on his head?

Dead.

"I'm ready for **you** now."

Headspeak:
Heads will roll.

The Head (skull, bonce, brain-case, boss, Master)

A creature that rises from the grave to drink the blood of the living and prey mercilessly on others. Stalks the unwary. Not often seen in daylight. Warning: Avoid being sent to visit the Head.*

*Not to be confused with head (loo) on boats (Ed.)

Headmaster:
"Boy, you should have been here an hour ago."
Boy:
"Why, what happened?"

53

Gym Mistress

Jolly, sporty type who organises outdoor games like Hockey and Netball. They make kids skip, hop, stretch, vault, run on the spot, and jog until they drop. Avoid – they are dangerously hyperactive. Will go white water rafting, potholing, and bungy jumping in their hols.

Net!

Bananas?
Our teacher went on a special banana diet. Did she lose weight? No, but she couldn't half climb trees!

Domestic Science Teacher

These teachers teach kids how and what to cook. They are extremely clean and like their food. Cooking is a bit like a chemistry lesson. You mix and stir things together, put them in the oven and stand well back.

It's toad in the hole, Miss.

Netball Really soppy boring game where you have to jump around and put a ball in a net 20ft off the ground. The only people who like netball are the fit healthy kids with long arms.

Hockey Game played with a stick and a bully. (See Bully)

Greedy Gag: There once was a schoolboy called kid.
Who ate 20 pies for a quid.
When asked, "Are you faint?"
He replied, "No I ain't.
But I don't feel as well as I did."

Foul Food
Please Miss, can I lick the bowl?
No, Sharon, flush it like the other kids.

With **real** toads.

School Dinners ...

After a hard morning of learning, kids need to eat. Some kids bring packed lunches: some have school dinners. Dinners at school can be really brill or seriously 'orrible. If the dinner ladies think you're sweet and need 'fattening up', you could get hamburgers and chips, sausage and chips, curry and chips, or fish and chips every day. But if the dinner ladies think you're a real slob, you will get cabbage, cabbage and cabbage.

It's yummy

School dinners make you sicker quicker.

I eat peas with honey.
I've done it all my life.
It makes the peas taste funny.
But it keeps them on the knife.

Dinner Ladies

Probably the most important people in
school. Never, never cheek a dinner lady.
Kids can get thin if they upset the dinner
ladies. They can also get more than their fair
share of cabbage (yuk!)

I feel sick.

Rotten Rhyme

Don't eat school Dinners
Just throw them aside,
A lot of kids didn't,
A lot of kids died.

The meat's made
of iron,
The spuds are
of steel.
And if they don't kill,
the pudding will!

Cabbage

Green, smelly and disgusting.
Teachers had to eat lots and lots
of this when they were kids.

Yuk!

Custard

Lumpy, yellow school pudding.
Chew well before eating
or swallowing.

Tortures

School can be torture, but long ago it was gruesome. Kids got bashed, birched, caned, clouted, larruped, lashed, slapped, slippered, smacked and strapped.

This is going to hurt me more than it will hurt you.

Lummy

Walloper's Wit: Spare the rod and spoil the child. You've got to be cruel to be kin

Cane

This popular instrument of torture was used by cruel teachers in ancient olden days (before colour TV was invented).

← Cruel teacher

As a rule I don't usually hit pupils, but in your case Buswell, I'm going to make an exception.

Yes Miss, thank you Miss

When do you like school most? At weekends, holidays and when I'm off sick.

Teachers often ruled by the ruler.

Rulers made a handy weapon for wicked teachers to rap the dim on the knuckles. (Very painful.)

Cretin's Corner

Putting kids in the corner kept them quiet.

Teachers were sometimes called Beaks in olden days. Can you think why this was?

The traditional Lughole pinch, twist and pull.

Any kids who upset teachers were liable to be dragged out by an ear. The result of this cruel torture could be why so many old people have big ears. Check out Granny and Grandad's lugs.

Cruel old teacher

Ooooow!

Cruel Crack: Why did so many children go to the headmaster's funeral? To make sure he was really dead.

Detention

Terrible punishment invented by cruel teachers – victim is imprisoned in classroom during break or after school hours.

Reports

Reports are the sneaky things that teachers write about kids to their parents. They make up lots of 'porky pies' in order to get kids into trouble.

Pay attention to avoid detention.

When I'm lying cold
and dead.
Put my school books
by my head.
Tell my teacher I've
got to rest.
And won't be back
for the English Test.

Dracula's School — Report —	
READING	Good
WRITING	Untidy
CRICKET	Shows promise as a bat

60

Lines

Rotten punishment given by cruel teachers where you get blistered fingers writing the same thing over and...over and...over and...over and...over and...over...again.

How are you getting on with your exams?
Not bad, the questions are easy – it's the answers I have difficulty with.

Exams

Form of cruel torture.
Exams are a test of
what you have learnt.
Or, more accurately,
what you can remember
of what you have learnt.
They always begin with
'write your name at the
top of the page'.

What is my name?

Test Teasers:
What exams do farmers take?
Hay Levels.

How do R.E.
Teachers mark exams?
With Spirit Levels.

Side Splitters
I hope I didn't
see you looking
at Tom's work?

I hope you
didn't
either, sir.

Expel

If you do something really bad at school,
like forget your homework twice in one
week, you could be expelled or turfed out
of school and never, never, never be allowed
back in. (Wow!)

Teacher's Prayer

One more day of sin.
One more day of sorrow.
One more day in
this old dump
And we stay at home
tomorrow.

Thank
goodness
for that!

I must not forget to do my homewo
I must not forget to do my homewor
I must not forget to do my homewor
I must not forget to do my homew
I must not forget to do my homewor
I must not forget to do my homework
I must not forget to do my homev
I must not forget to do my homewo
I must not forget to do my homewor
I must not forget to do my homewc
I must not forget to do homewor
I must not do my homework
I must not forget to do homen
I must not forget to do my homer
I must not forget to do my homewo
I must not forget to do my homewe
most not forget to do my homev
most not forget to do my homev
I must not forget to do my home

teech